PIXEL COLORING

C0-AKE-388

SECTION 1:
ANIMALS

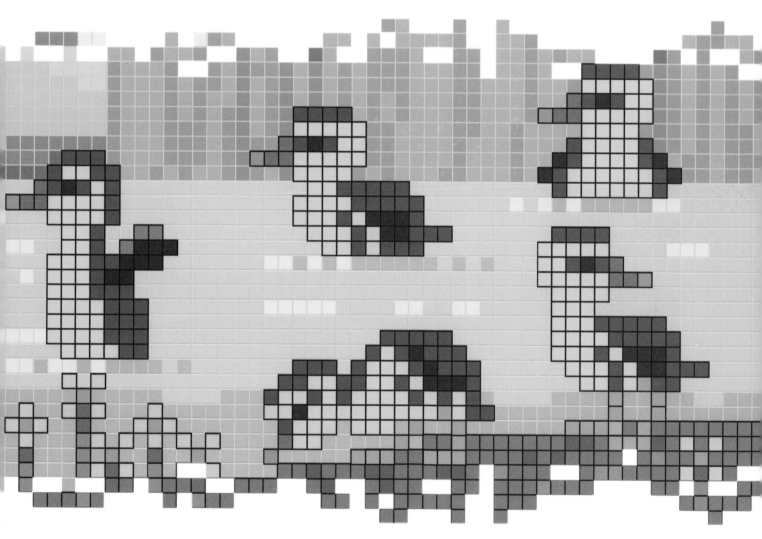

Sandy Creek
NEW YORK

An Imprint of Sterling Publishing
1166 Avenue of the Americas
New York, NY 10036

SANDY CREEK and the distinctive Sandy Creek logo are registered trademarks of Barnes & Noble, Inc.
Text © 2015 Tide Mill Media. Illustrations © 2015 Tide Mill Media
This 2015 edition published by Sandy Creek.
ISBN 978-1-4351-6274-7
Manufactured in Zhejiang, China
Lot #:
0 2 4 6 8 10 9 7 5 3 1
11/15

Snoozy Suzie

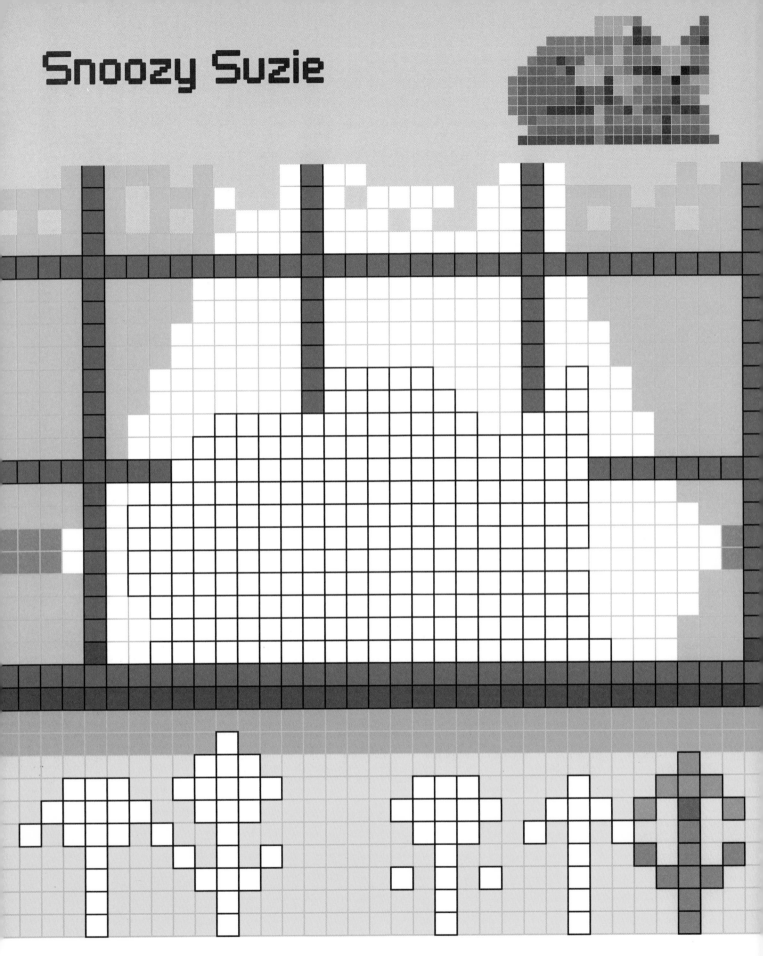

I'm a pretty kitty with soft fur and a gorgeous pink bow. I like nothing better than having a catnap on the sunny windowsill...purrrfect!

Playful Patch

I'm just a playful dog, always wagging my tail. When I see my favorite ball, I run around the backyard and bark. Woof, woof!

Buddy Birdsong

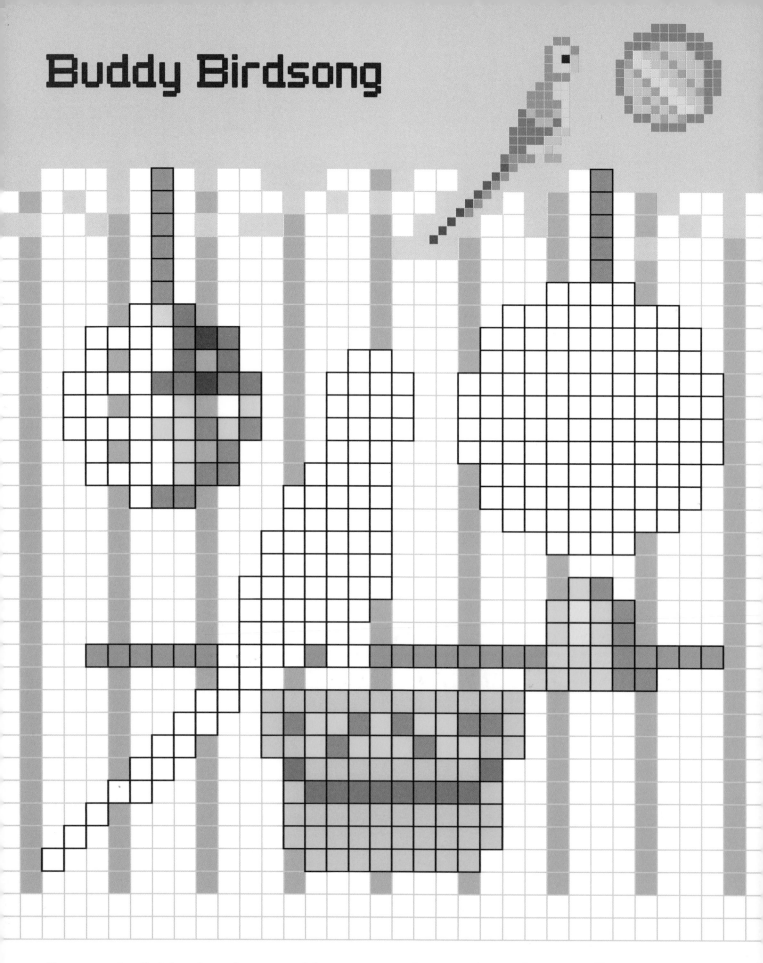

I'm a colorful budgerigar and I preen and stretch and tweet. I'm a pretty boy and I love looking at myself in the mirror...chirp, chirp, chirp!

Fab Fish!

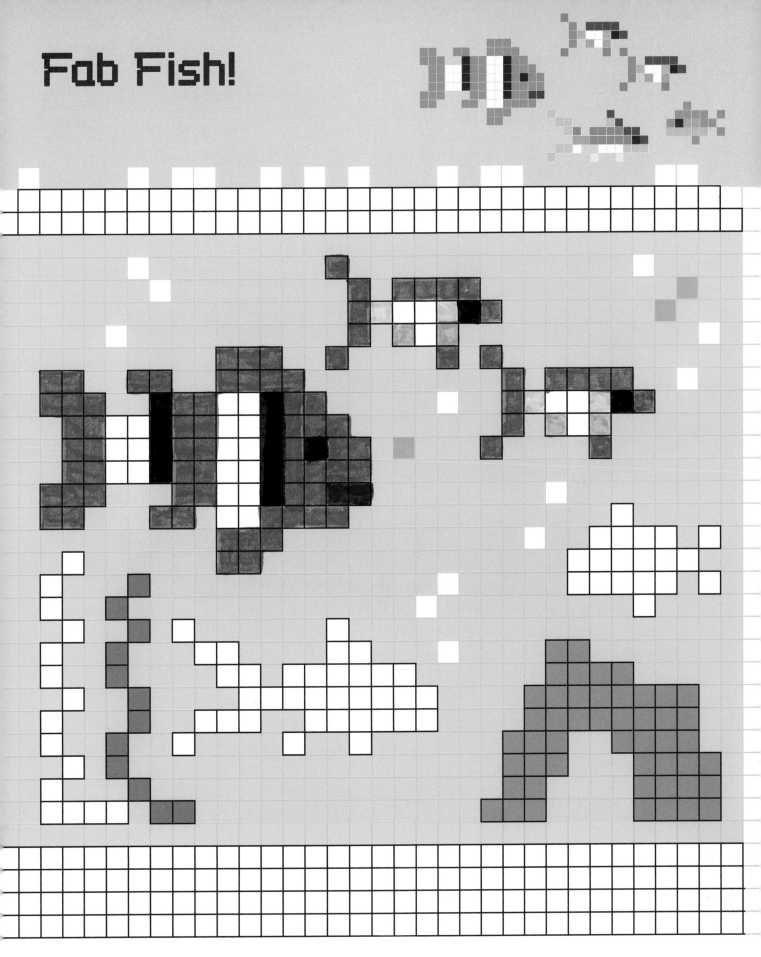

We are colorful fish of all shapes and sizes. We love hiding amongst the plants and rocks in our tank...bloop, bloop, bloop!

Nippy Nora

I'm a slippery terrapin and I love swimming in the water and sunning myself on a rock. Don't get your fingers too close. Snap!

Flopsie

I'm just a happy bunny rabbit and I love hopping around the backyard.
I get very excited when I see my favorite food...carrots!

Dear Ducks!

I'm a hungry duck with waterproof feathers and webbed feet. I love to preen my feathers to keep them shiny and clean.

We are little ducklings. We swim, swim, swim...looking for tasty plants and insects to eat. Peep, peep, peep!

Chatty Gabby

I'm a happy, chatty guinea pig and I nibble grass all day. I love crunchy fruit and vegetables as a very special treat. Yum!

Hungry Henry

I'm a lucky little hamster because I can store food in my stretchy cheeks.
I like to sleep during the day. At night I wake up and play! Squeak!

Chirpy Chicks

We are bundles of yellow feathery fun. Cheep, cheep, cheep! We won't stay like this for long, because we grow up very fast!

Lazy Daisy

I'm a friendly cow and I munch on grass all day. I give you milk for drinking— and making butter, cheese, and yogurt too.

Monty Mouse

I'm a pet mouse and I scurry and play in my cage. I love dawn and dusk, when I get up to mousy mischief! Squeak, squeak!

Field Mouse Family

We are a family of field mice. We live outdoors and hunt for yummy food like snails, seeds, and insects!

Fishy Friends

I'm Fancy Fifi, the biggest, prettiest fish in the aquarium. Just look at my fancy colors and patterns. Pretty me!

We are more pretty fish! We love swimming in the clear water, having fun with our fishy friends.

Dilly Dachshund

I'm a playful little hound with a long body and very short legs. I run to keep up with my owner when we go for walks. I have lots of energy!

Bouncy Benji

I'm a bouncy, yappy puppy dog. When I'm not chasing a ball, I'm busy chasing my tail! Yap, yap!

Nutty Nancy

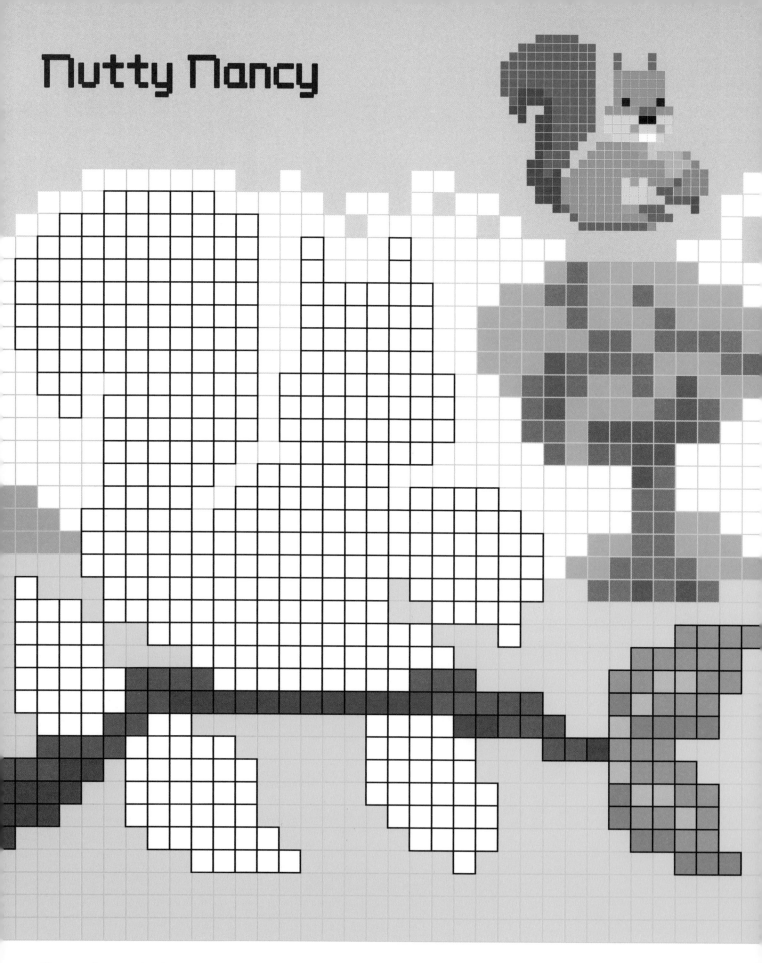

I'm a busy little squirrel and I'm nuts about nuts! I sometimes bury them to keep them safe. Now where did I hide the last one?

Foxy Felix

I'm such a handsome fox, with my big, bushy tail! I live in a beautiful park, close to town, where I hide in the daytime.

Penguin Pastimes

I'm a big daddy penguin with a very important job. I'm keeping an egg warm until my chick is ready to hatch. Peck, peck, peck!

We are happy penguin chicks, slipping, sliding, and skidding in the ice and snow. Wheeeee!

Eight-arms Amy

I'm an amazing octopus with eight wiggly, squiggly arms. I can hide by changing color to match my background. That's cool!

Snappy Stanley

I'm a snippety-snappety crab with clickety-clackety claws! I scuttle around the seashore, but I love rock pools best of all. Snip, snap!

Dolphin Friends

We are sleek and graceful dolphins. In and out of the waves we swim, hunting for fish and squid. Splish, splash, splosh!

We are all great friends! We love to spend time together, diving, splashing, and having fun!

Croaking Cuthbert

I'm a hungry green frog. I sit still on my lily pad, keeping a lookout for yummy flies. Croak, croak, croak!

Dainty Dora

I'm a shy little deer with a soft, velvety coat. I tiptoe through the trees nibbling grass, shoots, and leaves.

Slithering Sam

I'm a slithering, hissing snake. I glide through the forest, hunting for lizards, eggs, and frogs...and I swallow them whole! Gulp!

Toothy Terence

I'm a grinning crocodile with a mouth full of teeth. But beware of my smile, because I'm feeling hungry! SNAP!

Timmy Toucan

I'm a talkative toucan with an enormous colorful bill. It's perfect for reaching all the tasty fruit I like to eat.

Polly Parrot

I'm just a pretty parrot and I love to make noise.

Climbing Milo

I'm a fun-loving monkey with a very useful tail. It's awesome for climbing and swinging through the trees!

Gorgeous George

I'm a gorgeous gorilla—a very special beast. There aren't many of us left, so it's important for me to stay safe.

Enormous Ellie

I'm an enormous elephant with a super-amazing trunk. I use it for breathing, drinking, and holding things. Lucky me!

Towering Twins

We are giraffes—the tallest land animals in the whole world! We love the tastiest leaves from the highest trees. Munch, munch, munch!

Bright Butterflies

We are fluttering butterflies with beautiful, colorful wings. We fly from flower to flower, looking for sweet nectar to eat.

We love the warm summer sun and backyards full of pretty summer
flowers. Aren't we lovely?

Pink Patsy

I'm a pretty flamingo with pink feathers, and a long neck and legs. I wade in shallow water, scooping up food with my big bill.

Roaring Rex

I'm a big wild cat with an amazing furry mane. I hunt other animals and I have a very loud voice. Rooaaar!

Soaring Sidney

I'm a powerful bird of prey with big wings and excellent eyesight. I soar high in the sky, looking out for my next meal. Watch out below!

Hooting Harry

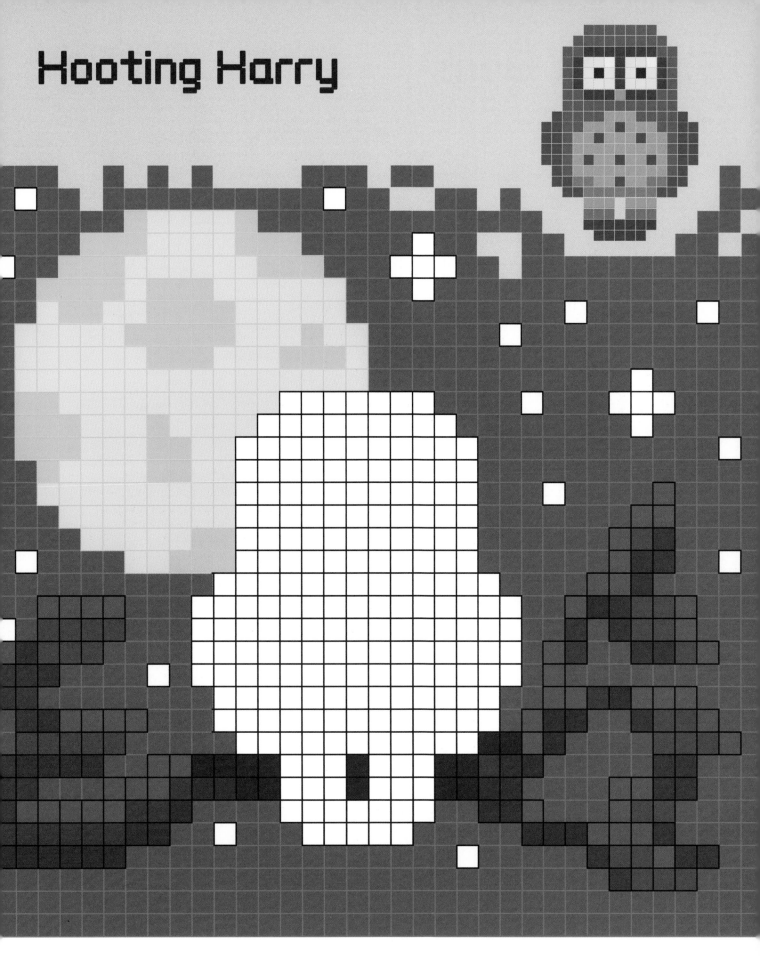

I'm a feathery owl and I come out at night. I love hunting in the moonlight, when you're fast asleep! Hoo-hoo!

Brilliant Bugs

I'm a red and black ladybug, so I'm easy to see! You'll find me crawling around the backyard and even hiding indoors!

We are more creepy-crawlies. You'll find us hiding in all kinds of places.
Spot us if you can!

Slow Seymour

I'm a slimy snail with my house on my back. I take life slowly as I crawl along, and I hide in my shell to keep safe.

Hopping Hattie

I'm a bouncy kangaroo with powerful legs and a long tail. I keep my baby safe in my pouch while he grows. Boing, boing, boing!

Humpy Hugo

I'm a big desert animal with a hump on my back. I can go without water for a long time, which is great for living in hot places!

PIXEL COLORING
SECTION 2:
PEOPLE

Dusty Stetson

I'm a fast-shootin' rancher from the old Wild West. I'm as tough as
old boots and quicker than a rattlesnake! Yee-hah!

Stumpy McPatch

I'm a swashbucklin' pirate with one eye and one leg. I sail the seven seas in search of gold doubloons. Aaaargh!

Pharaoh Nuff

I'm the greatest pharaoh that has ever ruled Ancient Egypt. My hobbies include building sandcastles and taking my pet lion for walks. Good kitty!

Max Speed

That's one small step for man, one giant leap for pixelkind!

Luke Out

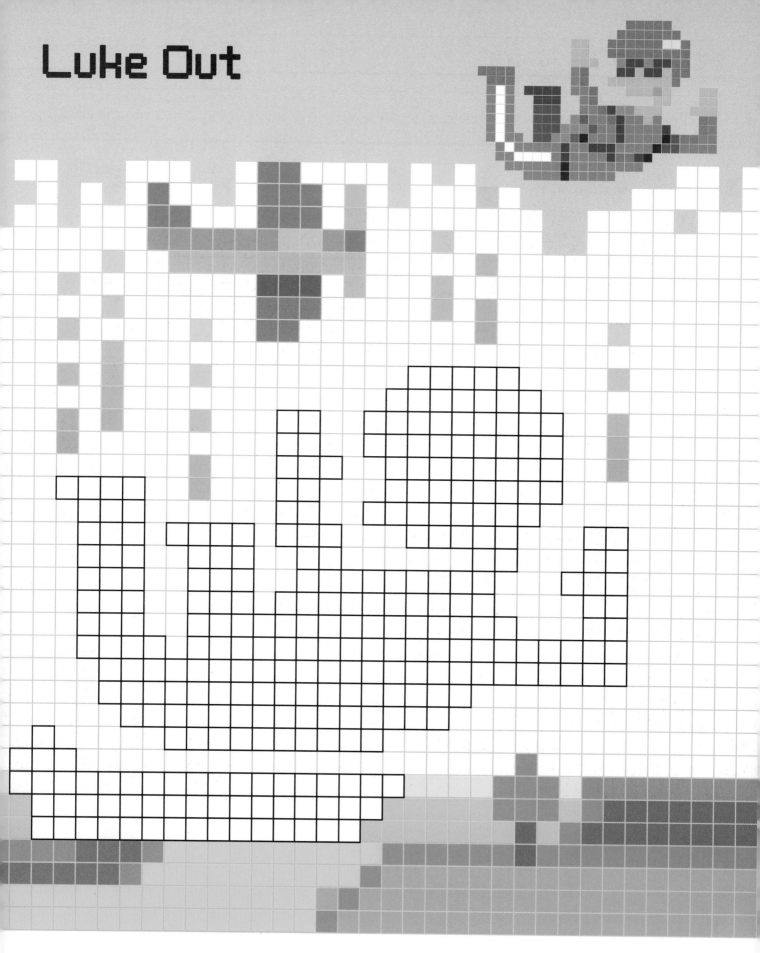

Sky diving is so much fun. Wait a minute, where's my parachute?

Mr. R. Otting

I used to be alive, but now I am a walking dead monster who loves to eat humans! Munch!

The Red Devil

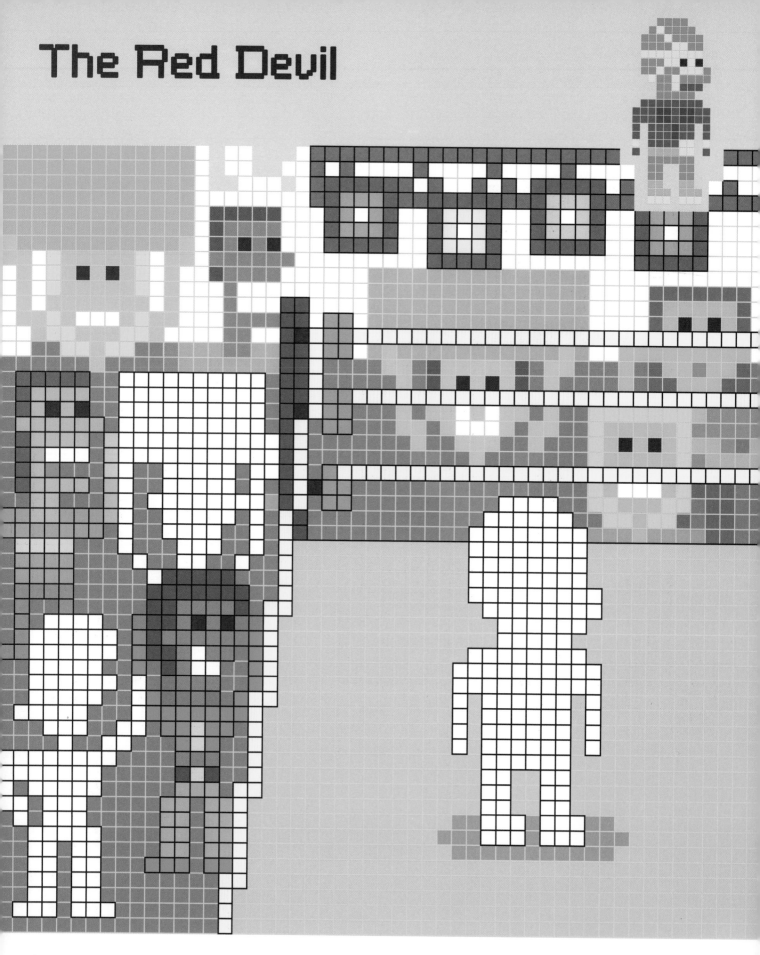

I, the Red Devil, have sworn to defeat my ultimate foe in one-on-one combat! Ha, ha, ha, ha!

The Masked Avenger

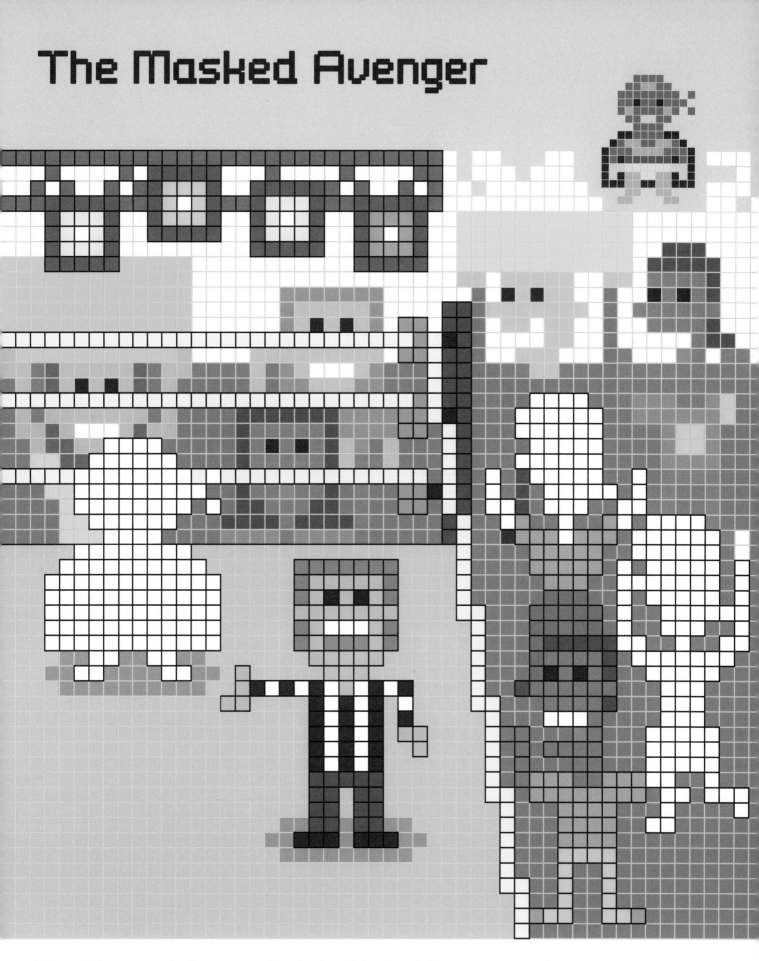

You will never defeat me, for I, the Masked Avenger, am the greatest wrestler ever! No really, I am, you can ask my mom.

Nick Money

Hands up! Your bunny or your life! I mean my life or your honey!
I mean...oh forget it.

Rod Steel

Between you and me, could you color me in some bigger muscles?

Mel Odey

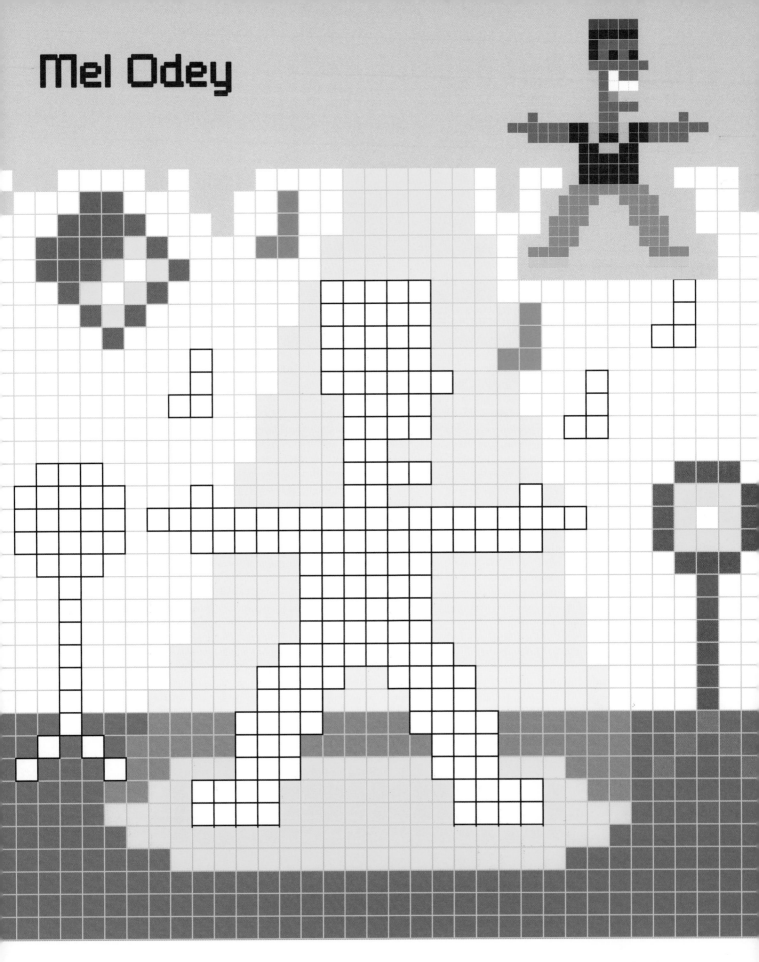

This next song is going out to the intelligent, good-looking kid with the pencils. That's you, dummy!

Count Sheep

I'm a blood-sucking vampire with a sleep problem. Well have you tried sleeping in the daytime?

Sue Perkid

I use my superpowers to fight crime and protect the innocent. Watch out, bad guys, here I come! Kapow!

Rusty Bolt

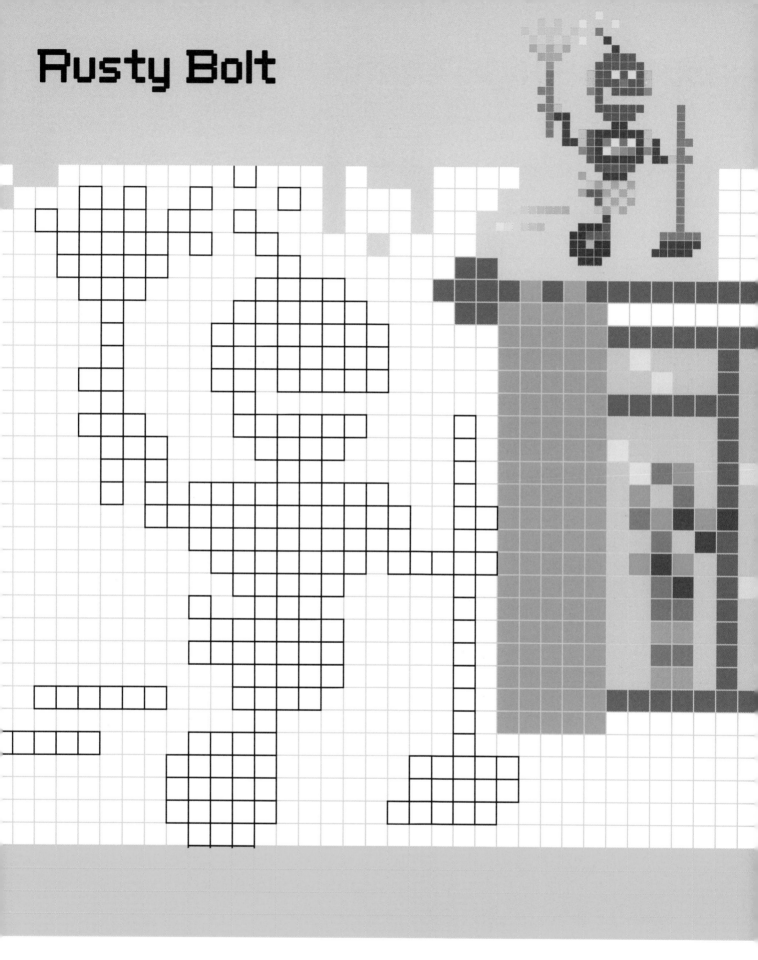

I am a helpful robot programmed to do all the jobs you don't want to.
I love tidying up, and doing homework. Beep beep!

King George the Quite Good

I'm the king, so everyone has to do what I tell them to. Now color me in—
and that's an order!

Queen Alice

I wish I'd married King Charles the Great. No one takes a "quite good" king seriously. Sigh...

Jock Power

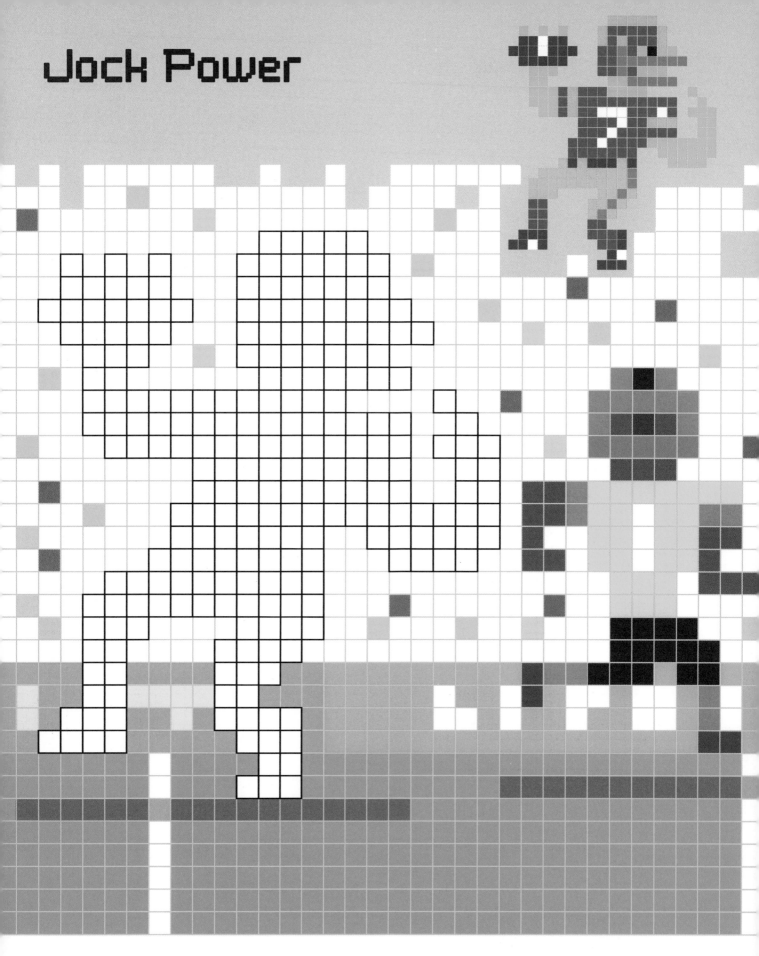

I'm the star quarterback of the team. Hut, hut, hike!

Master Piece

Hello! I am a very famous painter. I would like to paint you.
Your face is very strange and interesting.

Victoria de Boulderdash

I'm a princess and I live in a huge palace, full of old things. It's so boring!
I love ponies, flowers, and sparkly tiaras. Ding-a-ling-aling—it's teatime!

Chuck Danger

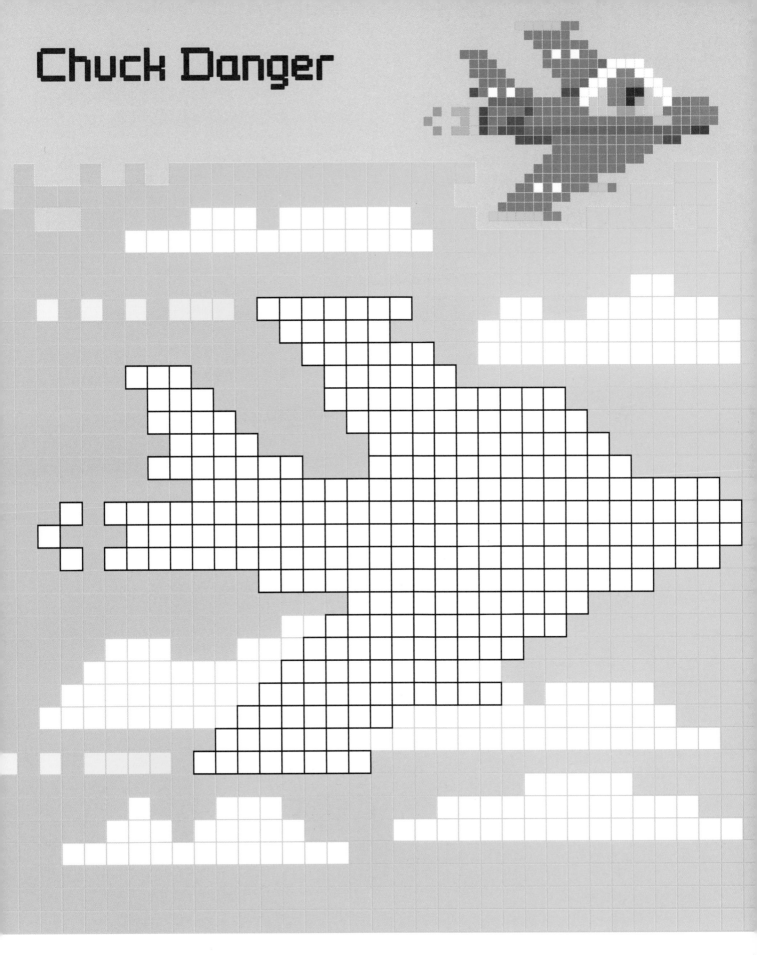

Hey, Chuck Danger here. I'm a fighter pilot. I feel the need, the need for speed! Vroom!

Serge Up

I am the world's most famous climber, and I have climbed all the highest peaks and most dangerous mountains.

Sherpa Sum Mit

I have climbed them all too!

Plenty O'Bubbles

Blub blub blub. Blub blub blub, blub, blub blub. Blub blub blub blub blub!

Mr. S. P. Ells

Stand back! I'm about to summon my breakfast. Toastandjellio!

Erik the Angry

My favorite things are raiding, plundering, fighting, and kittens.
WHAT'S SO FUNNY?

Maximus Pugnacius

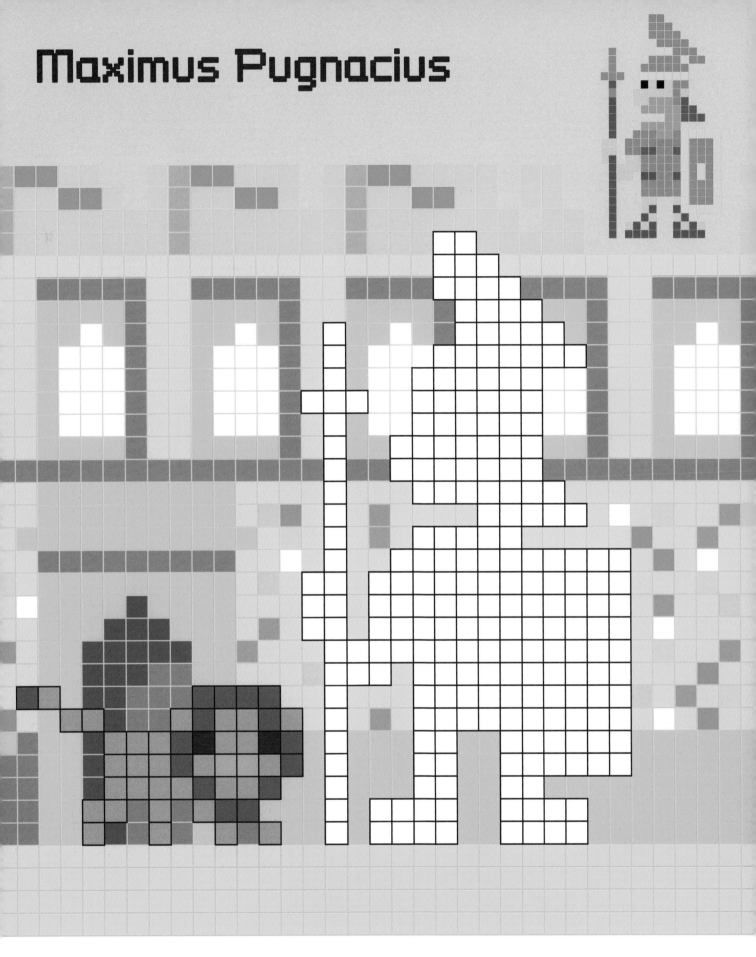

The Roman army is famous for its discipline. We always tidy up after fighting.

Hairy Styles

When the full moon rises something terrible happens.
Don't get too close, I bite!

Anne Teak

I've been sleeping for thousands of years. Now someone has woken me up...and I'm not very happy!

Rob A. House

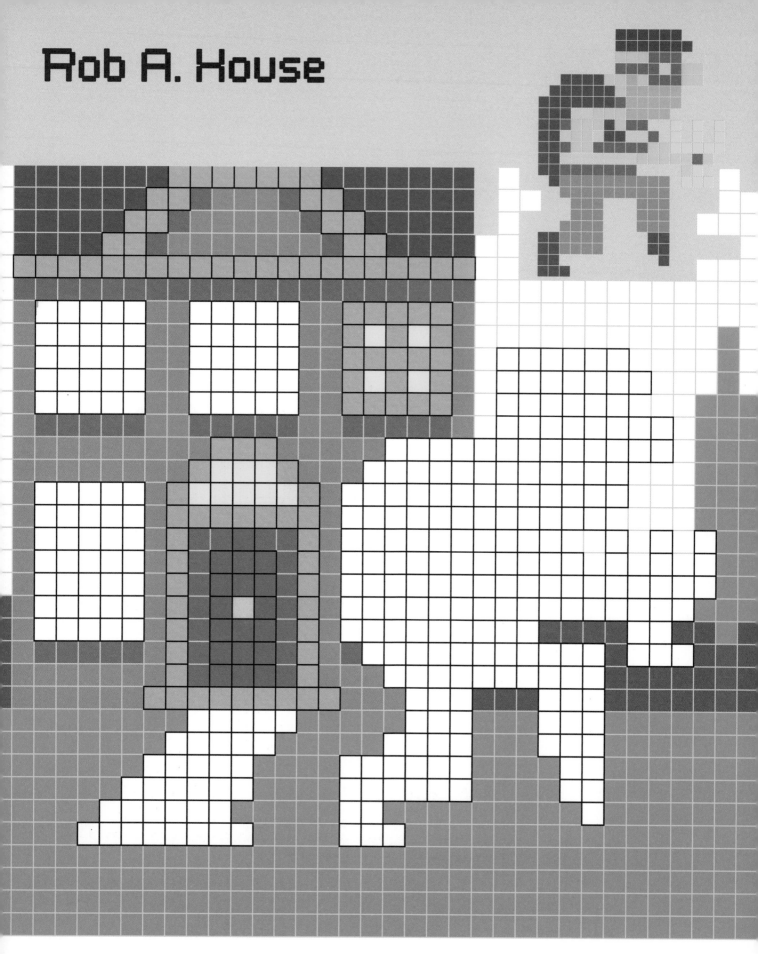

I'm just borrowing this...don't tell anybody.

Miss N. Chanter

You don't want to mess with me. I once turned a tadpole into a frog!

Tommy Rocket

Hey everybody, put on your leather pants and get ready to rock out!
Tommy Rocket is here to party!

Jeet Kun Who

I am a deadly ninja and can move invisibly. You can see me? Umm...

Sir Lee

I'm a bad tempered knight from days of old. I love to fight and I'm the best jouster in the kingdom!

Sir Prise

Ha! I'll show you who's the best, you scoundrel! I challenge you to a pixel joust!

The Incredible Ian

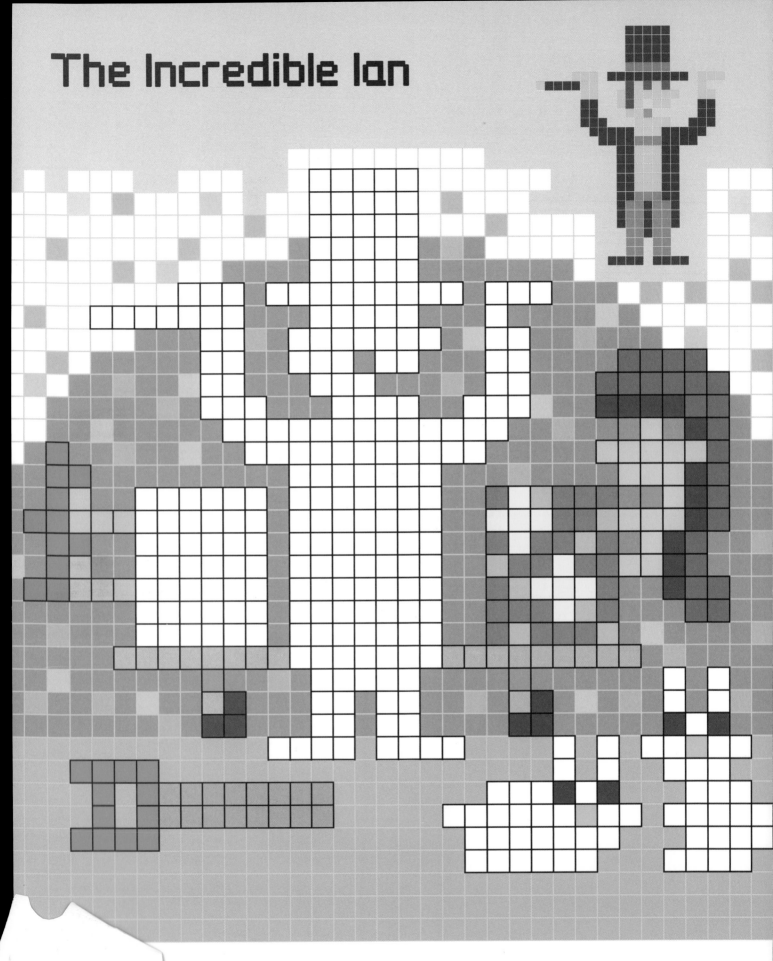

ow how to saw a person in half. Next week I'm learning how to
ck together again.

Captain Joe

Soldiers sing when they run,
Pixel Pix is really fun!

Ray Sing

I'm about to jump this here canyon on ma' bike. It looks bigger than I thought it was. Gulp!

Mike At

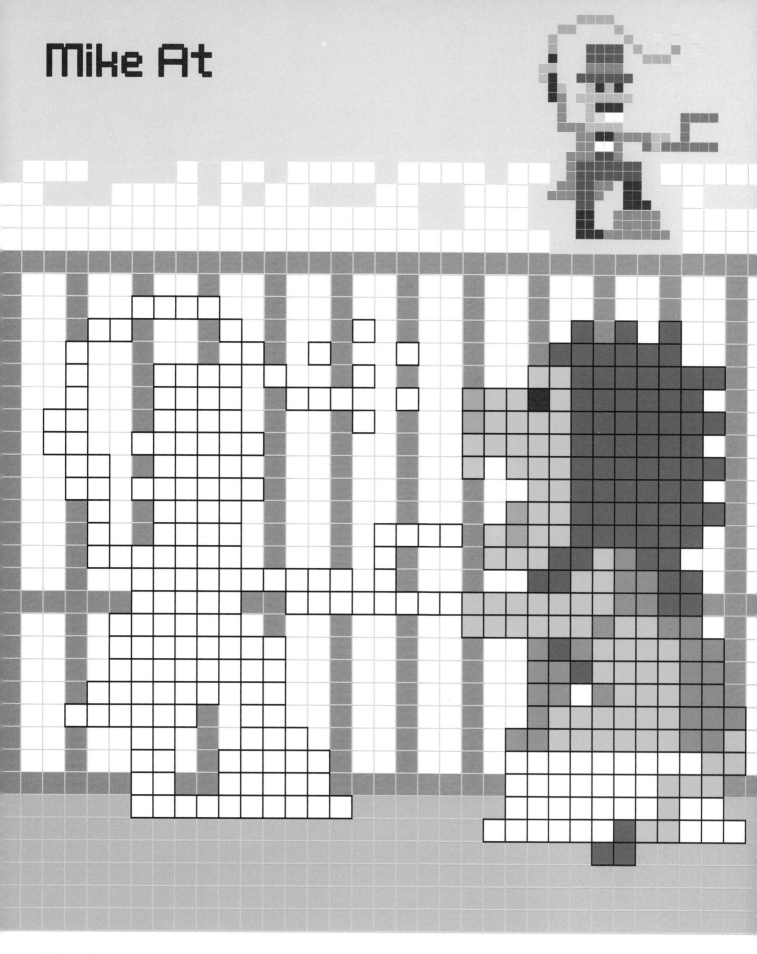

The clowns in my circus are all safe. Lions won't eat them.
They taste funny!

Dr. Chop

Don't worry, I've seen this operation before in a movie.

Nurse Worse

It's hard work being a nurse! There's always lots of people to help.
Um, are you sure that's right, Doctor?

Eva Searching

I've been exploring this jungle for over five years. Actually, this is a bit embarrassing, but I'm completely lost!

Cave Man

Ugg ugg. Ugg ugg ugg ugg uggg uggggg!

Yaron Mars

My squadron has been scrambled. There's an alien invasion!

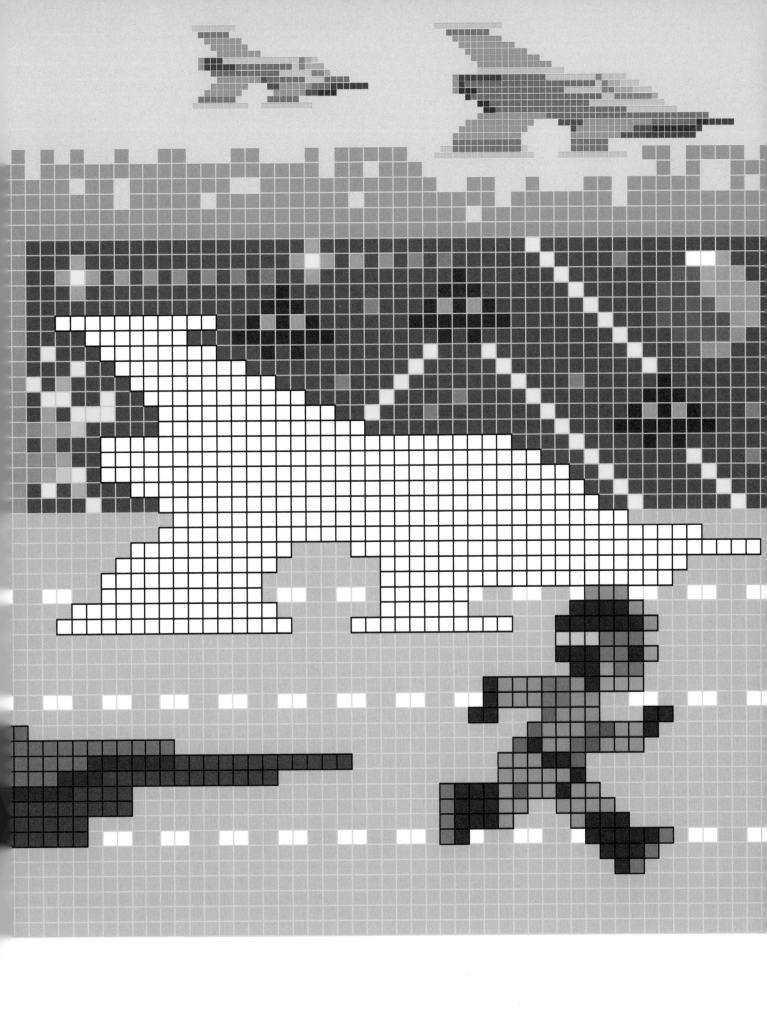

Arthur Brick

I can build you a house, no problem. I just need some help coloring it in!

Hugh Mongous

I'm a friendly giant, but every time I meet someone new they run away screaming. Will you be my friend?